Editor
Lorin Klistoff, M.A.

Managing Editor
Karen Goldfluss, M.S. Ed.

Illustrator
Mark Mason

Cover Artist
Brenda DiAntonis

Art Manager
Kevin Barnes

Art Director
CJae Froshay

Imaging
Alfred Lau
Rosa C. See

Publisher
Mary D. Smith, M.S. Ed.

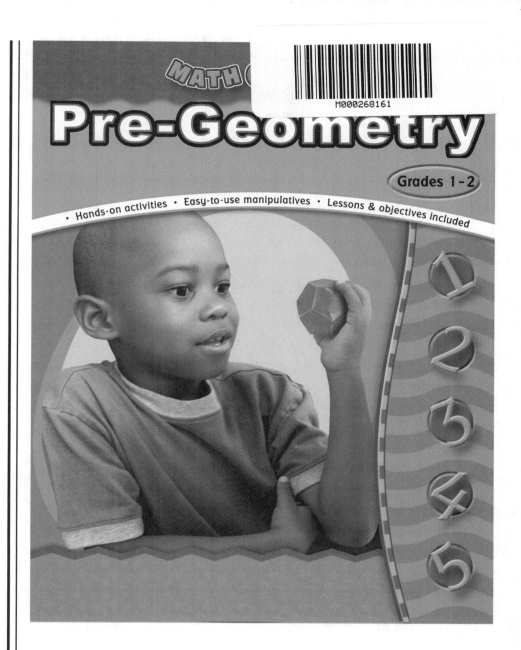

Pre-Geometry

Grades 1-2

· Hands-on activities · Easy-to-use manipulatives · Lessons & objectives included

Author

Bev Dunbar

(Revised and rewritten by Teacher Created Resources, Inc.)

This edition published by *Teacher Created Resources, Inc.*
6421 Industry Way
Westminster, CA 92683
www.teachercreated.com

ISBN-1-4206-3531-X

©2005 Teacher Created Resources, Inc.

Made in U.S.A.

Teacher Created Resources

Table of Contents

#3531 Math in Action

Introduction

Pre-geometry is one of the most creative mathematical areas as it can link directly to your visual arts program. It is also packed full of special language that helps your students make sense of their world.

This book contains many action-packed lesson plans for manipulating pre-geometry concepts in fun, practical ways. Any additional resources required are easy-to-find classroom or household objects. The flexible activities range from simple to challenging, to help support different ability groups.

Making your teaching life easier is a major aim of the *Math In Action* series. This book is divided into units—each packed with manipulatives to explore, such as activity cards and worksheets for small groups or a whole class. You will find easy-to-follow instructions, with assessment help in the form of clearly stated skills. (See the complete list on page 95.)

Each activity is designed to maximize the way in which your students construct their own understandings about pre-geometry. Activities are open-ended and encourage students to think and work mathematically. Many of the activities in this book allow students to identify and investigate the properties of two-dimensional (2-D) and three-dimensional (3-D or solid) shapes. The emphasis is on practical manipulation of materials and the development of language and recording skills.

This book is a nice companion to TCR 3533 *Math in Action: Graphs, Data and Chance.*

Using these activities, your students will enjoy exploring pre-geometry concepts.

How to Use This Book

❑ **Teaching Lessons**

Many exciting lessons have been placed into nine units to assist with whole-class or small-group lessons. Each activity has clearly stated learning skills and easy-to-follow instructions. Activities generally are open ended and encourage your students to think for themselves.

❑ **Reproducible Pages**

There are four types of reproducible pages:

1. *Activity Pages*

   (e.g., page 7, *Sort Me)*
   These support your free exploration as well as your structured activities. Laminate these pages for reuse with small groups.

2. *Playing Cards*

   (e.g., page 11, *Sides)*
   Cut these cards out, shuffle, and use over and over again for small group games. Photocopy each set in different colors to assist in class management.

3. *Activity Cards*

   (e.g., page 66, *Sticks)*
   Use these cards for an additional stimulus in group work. The language is simple and easy to follow. Encourage your students to invent their own tasks too. You can laminate these cards for years of reuse.

4. *Reusable Worksheets*

   (e.g., page 94, *Find the Treasure)*
   Unlike normal worksheets, these sheets allow for different solutions and can be used by the same students again with different results.

❑ **Skills Record Sheet**

The complete list of learning outcomes is available on page 95. Use this sheet to record individual student progress. Try to assess a few students each day.

❑ **Sample Weekly Lesson Plan**

On page 96, you will find an example of how to organize a selection of activities for a five-day unit for your class.

Sorting and Classifying Shapes

In this unit, students will do the following:

- Sort, match, name, and draw 2-D shapes
- Identify corners and sides on 2-D shapes
- Identify 2-D faces of 3-D objects
- Sort, compare, and describe 3-D objects
- Recognize and name simple 3-D objects
- Match 3-D objects with 2-D drawings and photographs

(For skills used in this section, refer to the Skills Record Sheet on page 95.)

Sort Me

Skills

- Identify 2-D faces of 3-D objects
- Sort, match, name, and draw 2-D shapes

Grouping

- whole class
- small groups

Materials

- various classroom objects
- attribute blocks
- magazines
- Sort Me activity sheet (page 7)
- paper
- glue
- scissors
- painting equipment

Directions

- Ask students, "How many different names for flat shapes do you know?" (e.g., circles, squares, triangles) Have students point out where they can see some of these objects around the room.

- Discuss with students the shape of rectangles in particular.
  Ask, "What makes them different from squares?" (e.g., They are longer.)

- Demonstrate how to identify the shapes of flat faces of objects by painting on them, then printing them on paper.

- Form four small groups for rotating activities:

  1. Sort/paint/print flat faces from 3-D objects onto paper.

  2. Sort/trace outlines of 3-D shapes (e.g., attribute blocks) onto paper.

  3. Cut/sort/paste shapes from magazines.

  4. Cut/paste shapes from the Sort Me activity sheet to make pictures. (e.g., dog, house, or person)

Variations

- Students collect and sort examples of various 2-D shapes in a large class book. (e.g., drawings, picture cut-outs, face prints)

- Students bake biscuits in a variety of geometric shapes. Have students sort them into groups by shape and decorate with colored icing. (e.g., Make all the triangles red.)

Corner Hunt

Skills
- Sort, match, name, and draw 2-D shapes
- Identify corners and sides on 2-D shapes

Grouping
- whole class
- small groups

Materials
- paper clips
- pencils
- Corner Hunt spinners (page 9)
- a saucer or other round, flat object

Directions
- Ask students, "What is a corner?" (e.g., A corner is a place where two sides meet.) Have students stand up and move to a corner of the room.
- Trace around a saucer—or other round, flat object—on the chalkboard to make a circle. Ask students, "Do shapes like these have corners? Why? Why not? (e.g., A circle has one curved side but no corners and no points.) Ask, "Can you think of a shape that has two corners?" (e.g., half a circle)
- Ask students to close their eyes. Have them think of a straight-sided shape that has exactly three corners. Ask them to open their eyes. Have students draw this shape as large as they can in the air. Ask, "What shape did you draw?"
- Ask students to close their eyes again. Ask them to think of a straight-sided shape that has exactly four corners. Ask them to open their eyes. Ask someone to draw this shape on the chalkboard. Ask, "How many different shapes can you draw that have exactly four corners? Can you see one near you?"
- Have students go on a corner hunt. Have them find straight-sided shapes and count the corners. Ask, "Can you find a shape with five corners?" Discuss their shapes together. Ask, "How many sides on each of your shapes?"

Variations
- Ask students, "Do all shapes with three corners have three straight sides?"
- Have students investigate special names for four-sided shapes.

square $\square$ rectangle $\boxed{}$ diamond $\diamond$

- Students color and cut out the spinners. Have them place a paper clip through a tip of a pencil. Then, place the pencil at the center of the spinner and spin the paper clip. (See sample illustration.)

  $\bigcirc$ Means a shape with no corners.   ✳ Means a straight-edged shape with six or more corners.

Students take turns spinning the spinner and finding a shape with matching corners in the room. Ask, "How many corners does it have? How many sides?"

Spinner Directions

Color and cut out the
spinner. Put a paper clip
over the tip of a pencil.
Place the tip of the
pencil on the center of
the spinner and spin the
paper clip.

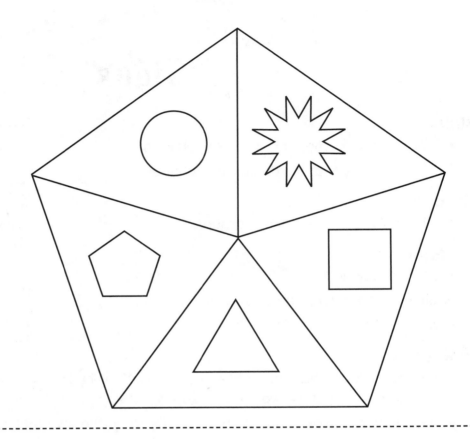

Spinner Directions

Color and cut out the
spinner. Put a paper clip
over the tip of a pencil.
Place the tip of the
pencil on the center of
the spinner and spin the
paper clip.

Sides

Skills
- Sort, match, name, and draw 2-D shapes
- Identify corners and sides on 2-D shapes

Grouping
- whole class
- small groups

Materials
- a beach towel
- Sides playing cards (pages 11 and 12)
- workbooks and pencils

Directions
- Ask students, "What shape is a beach towel? Why is it like this?" (e.g., It fits the length of your body. A circle would take up a lot of space on the sand.)
- Ask students, "How many corners are there on the towel? How many sides? What else has exactly four corners and four sides?" (e.g., a sheet of paper, a computer disk)
- Ask students to draw a three-sided shape. Ask someone to find or draw a different three-sided shape. Have them count the corners. Ask, "What do you notice?" (e.g., If there are three sides, there are three corners.)
- Ask students, "What is a side? How do you know where a side starts or ends?" Have students look for three-sided shapes around them.
- Form small groups and give each group a set of Sides playing cards. Have students count the number of corners and sides on each shape. Have them sort the cards into matching groups.
- Have students draw some of their shapes in their workbooks and record how many corners and how many sides. Have students draw more matching shapes for each group.
- Have students try to discover an example of each group in real life. (e.g., The drain in my sink is a hexagon—It has six corners and six sides.)

Variation
- Sides Challenge: Have students work in small groups. Have them shuffle the Sides cards, then turn over the top card. Tell them to race to draw a matching shape. Tell them that they score five points if it is exactly the same shape and 10 points if it has the same number of sides and corners, but it looks different.

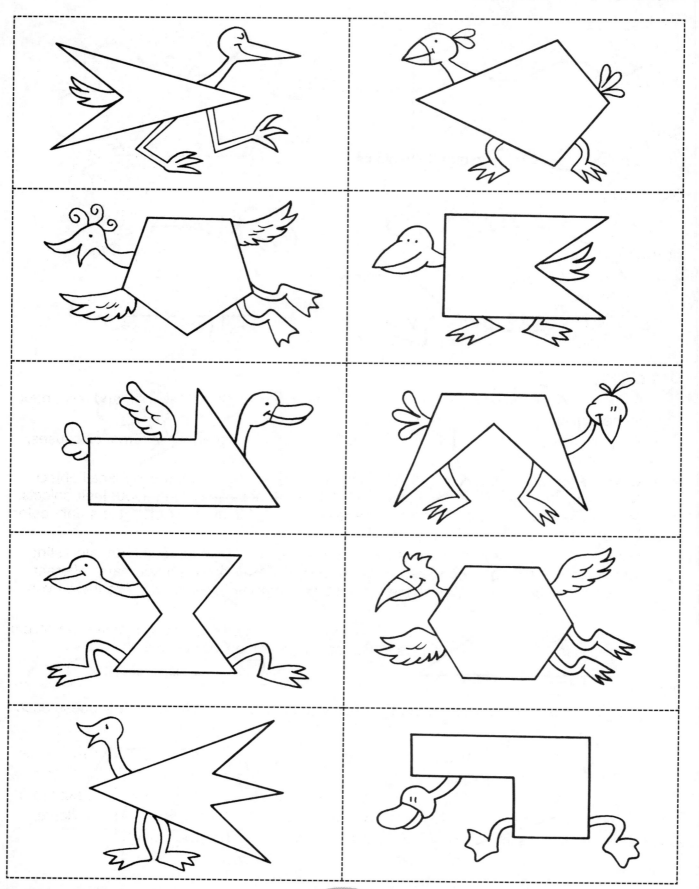

Describe It

Skill

- Sort, compare, and describe 3-D objects

Grouping

- whole class
- pairs

Materials

- random classroom objects (e.g., blocks, toys, home objects)
- pencils
- What Did I Buy? worksheet (page 14)

Directions

- Pass a variety of objects around the class. Ask everyone to look at, feel, and talk about these objects.
- Ask, "What sort of things did you describe?" (e.g., colors, shapes, textures, size, uses, heaviness)
- Give everyone a minute to stand up, walk around, and find an interesting small object. Now have students sit down in pairs and tell their partners everything about their objects. (e.g., a chalkboard eraser—It's hard, made of wood but soft on the top. It is a dark color. It is about as long as my foot.)
- Have students go out to the playground. Give everyone a minute to find an interesting large object. With a partner, have students describe their objects in as many different ways as they can. Ask, "What's the largest thing someone described? Are there even more ways you could talk about it?"
- Play a guessing game back in the classroom. Ask someone to describe a familiar object to the class. Ask, "Can you guess the object in fewer than 10 guesses?"

Variations

- Students describe objects around their home to their family. Ask, "Can they guess each object in less than one minute?"
- Students play What Did I Buy? (page 14) in small groups. Have them fold the worksheet in half. Have students open it up and draw a secret shopping item on the inside. (e.g., a large red car, a spiky hairdo) Have them close their worksheet. Their group asks them to describe their secret object. (e.g., "What shape is it? What color?") Ask students, "How many questions were asked before someone guessed your object?"

What Did I Buy?

What Did I Buy?

Where Does It Belong?

Skill

- Sort, compare, and describe 3-D objects

Grouping

- whole class
- small groups

Materials

- a collection of mixed objects for each group (e.g., blocks, toys, cartons, shells)
- Where Does It Belong? worksheet (page 16)

Directions

- Reveal a collection of mixed objects. Tell students someone threw everything together instead of packing them away neatly. Tell students to look at each object carefully. Ask, "Do any of the objects belong together?" (e.g., all the blocks) Discuss different sorting possibilities.

- Tell students to imagine they secretly sort these objects into two piles. They sort them in a way they think no one else has thought of. Ask, "How would you do this?"

- Tell students to whisper their secret sorting idea to the person next to them. (e.g., Put all large objects here. Put small objects there.) Ask, "Did anyone's partner think of your idea?" Ask students to think of another way to sort these objects.

- Discuss some class sorting suggestions. (e.g., objects with holes/without holes, red/not red objects)

- Form small groups. Give each group a collection of mixed objects. Have students secretly discuss how they will sort their objects into two piles. Have them sort, then count the number of objects in each group. Ask, "Which pile has more objects?" Tell them to ask another team to guess their sorting idea.

- Have students record their secret sort on the Where Does It Belong? worksheet. Then students draw a picture of one or more of the objects from their first pile in the box on the left and draw pictures of objects from their second pile in the box on the right.

Variation

- Students think of a secret sorting idea. (e.g., has metal on it/doesn't have metal; solid/hollow) Have them sort some objects into their two groups. Then they hold up a new object. Ask, "Where does this belong?" Ask different students to guess their sorting idea and predict which group it belongs in.

15

#3531 Math in Action

©Teacher Created Resources, Inc.

Spin-a-Shape

Skills

- Recognize and name simple 3-D objects
- Match 3-D objects with 2-D drawings and photographs

Grouping

- small groups

Materials

- one-minute timer
- paper and pencils
- magazines, scissors, glue, paper
- a mixed collection of spheres, boxes, blocks, cylinders, and other shapes
- Spin-a-Shape spinners (page 18) cut out, laminated, pencils, paper clips

Directions

- **Game 1**

  Each group needs a mixed collection of objects and a timer. Have each student spin the spinner and start the timer. The student must race to collect as many shapes that match the spinner as he or she can before the timer stops. Ask, "Who collected the most examples? Who collected the tiniest example? Who collected the largest example?"

  Note: When ⁂ appears on the spinner, have students think of a shape that is not a sphere, not a box, and not a cylinder. (e.g., a cone, a triangular prism, or a pyramid)

- **Game 2**

  Each student needs paper and a pencil. Each student spins the spinner. This time, he or she draws a picture of a shape he or she can see in the classroom that matches the shape on the spinner.

- **Game 3**

  Each student spins the spinner. This time, he or she names a real-life object that is not in the classroom that matches the shape on the spinner.

Variations

- A student from each group spins the spinner. Students race to look through magazines for a matching shape to cut out. Students decide as a group how they will make a group display from their cut-outs.
- Students construct their own spinner with pictures of other simple shapes they know. (e.g., a pyramid, a cone, a triangular prism)

Spinner Directions

Color and cut out the spinner. Put a paper clip over the tip of a pencil. Place the tip of the pencil on the center of the spinner and spin the paper clip.

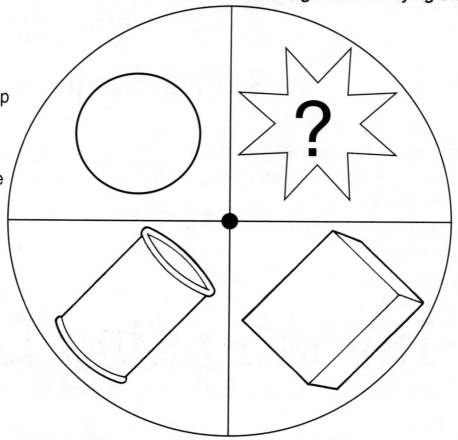

Spinner Directions

Color and cut out the spinner. Put a paper clip over the tip of a pencil. Place the tip of the pencil on the center of the spinner and spin the paper clip.

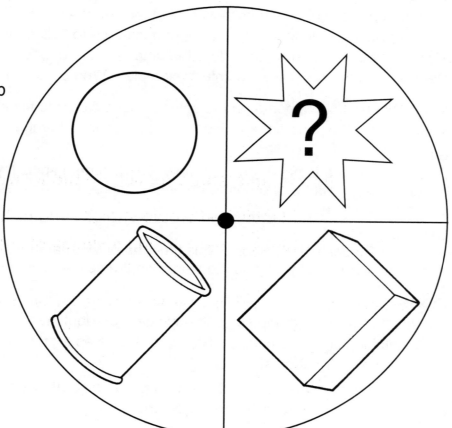

Investigating Lines

In this unit, students will do the following:

- Identify and create straight and curved lines
- Make patterns using a variety of lines

(For skills used in this section, refer to the Skills Record Sheet on page 95.)

Hairy

Skills

• Identify and create straight and curved lines

Grouping

• whole class

Materials

• pencils
• paper or workbooks
• Hairy worksheet (page 21)

Directions

• Tell students that their hair is made up of strands. Explain how some are straight and some are curly, some are short and some are long. Using your hand as a paintbrush, paint a huge straight strand of hair in the air. Paint a huge curved strand.

• Tell students to imagine if these strands were a different shape. Paint a wiggly strand in the air. Ask, "What other sorts of lines can you draw?" Discuss and demonstrate.

• Tell students to imagine their hair grew in spirals. Paint a spiral in the air. Ask, "Which way does your spiral turn?" Explain how some spirals turn to the right. Some spirals turn to the left. Students practice drawing spirals in the air and on paper.

• Paint a strand of hair like a spring. Ask, "What else does this remind you of?" (e.g., a telephone cord) Students practice drawing springy lines on their paper.

• Paint a line like a castle wall in the air. Ask, "What else does this remind you of?" (e.g., a set of teeth) Students practice drawing lines like this on their paper.

• Paint a jagged line. Ask, "What does this remind you of?" (e.g., shark's teeth, mountains) Students practice drawing zigzags on their paper.

• Students invent other strands of hair to draw. Have students practice in the air first. Students can share their line drawings with a friend.

Variation

• Students use the Hairy worksheet. Give instructions on how to draw each strand of hair. (e.g., "Make all the hair zigzags." Or, "Draw the first strand straight and the second strand like a spring.")

#3531 Math in Action

Zebras

Skills

- Identify and create straight and curved lines
- Make patterns using a variety of lines

Grouping

- whole class

Materials

- pictures/posters of a zebra *(optional)*
- Zebras worksheet (page 23)
- pencils and paper

Directions

- Ask students to close their eyes. Have them think of an animal with stripes. Ask them to open their eyes and tell the person next to them about their animal. Ask, "How many different animals have stripes? Why do you think they have stripes on their body?"

- Have students draw what a stripe looks like in the air. Ask, "Does a stripe go across or down or both? How else can a stripe go?" (e.g., It can slope.)

- Have students discuss the stripes on a zebra. (e.g., They go all around the different parts of a zebra's body. They are different thicknesses.)

- Ask students to imagine there is a way to make the stripes on a zebra change. Ask, "How else could you draw lines? Can stripes be curly? Can they be broken?"

- Have students experiment on paper with different ways to make a pattern from stripes. Ask, "What happens if you combine straight and curved lines? What happens if the lines cross over?"

- Have students find a way to sort the different patterns they have made. Make a class display.

Variation

- Students use the Zebras worksheet. Have them record their new line patterns on their zebra. Ask, "Can you cover the whole body with this pattern?"

Repeat It

Skills

- Identify and create straight and curved lines
- Make patterns using a variety of lines

Grouping

- whole class
- small groups

Materials

- pictures or objects with real-life repeating line patterns (e.g., vases, dress materials, human bodies)
- Repeat It worksheet (page 25)

Directions

- Ask students, "Why do people decorate objects?" (e.g., People decorate objects to make them colorful and interesting.) Tell students humans have always been decorating things around them. (e.g., Archaeologist have found decorative line patterns on fish hooks, pottery, and jewelery from over 20,000 years ago.)
- Ask students, "What things in your home have patterns made from repeating lines?" Discuss everyday objects. (e.g., plates, cups, and saucers)

- Tell a partner how to decorate each of the items on the Repeat It worksheet. (e.g., Draw sloping straight lines on the vase.)

Variations

- Students imagine they are decorating a wall. They paint their own line patterns on large sheets of paper.
- Students investigate patterns made by repeating whole shapes. Ask, "Where can you find these patterns in real life?"

Investigating Patterns

In this unit, students will do the following:

- Make, describe, copy, and extend patterns using 3-D objects

- Identify, continue, and predict 2-D patterns

- Flip, slide, and turn 2-D shapes to construct patterns

- Tessellate 2-D shapes to make patterns

(For skills used in this section, refer to the Skills Record Sheet on page 95.)

26

A Secret Pattern

Skills

- Make, describe, copy, and extend patterns using 3-D objects

Grouping

- whole class
- pairs

Materials

- a "magic" cloth (e.g., a dish towel)
- groups of 3-D objects (e.g., buttons, shells, blocks, crayons)
- construction toys (e.g., plastic building bricks, multilinks)
- A Secret Pattern cards (page 28)

Directions

- Show students the "magic" cloth. Tell students to imagine this is a special cloth that puts things under it into a pattern. Ask, "What is a pattern? What is not a pattern? How do you know?"
- Secretly make a pattern with several objects under the cloth. (e.g., button, shell, block, button, shell, block) Reveal the pattern and talk about it.
- Challenge someone else to make a different pattern under the cloth. (e.g., red block, red block, yellow block, blue block) Ask another person to continue this pattern.
- Ask, "What are different ways you can make a pattern?" (e.g., change colors, shapes, sizes; put some things upside down; use different quantities)
- Have each student decide on a pattern to make with a partner. Tell students that when they have about six or more objects, they should challenge another team to continue their pattern.

Variation

- Pattern Challenge: This is suitable with parent helpers or if you have a strong reader in the group. Students work in pairs as part of a small group. Students shuffle the cards and place them face down in the center. Everyone makes a pattern with at least six objects in it. Somebody turns over the top card and reads out the instruction. Students try to follow the instructions with their pattern and their partner. (e.g., Hide two objects—their partner has to tell them what is hidden by looking at the other objects left in their pattern.)

    ⭐? means students make up their own pattern challenge.

Copy my pattern.

Continue my pattern.

Make a new pattern.

Change my pattern.

Talk about my pattern.

Hide one object.

Hide two objects.

What's My Pattern?

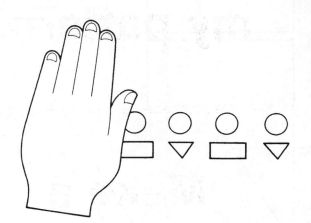

Skills
- Identify, continue, and predict 2-D patterns

Grouping
- whole class
- individuals

Materials
- pattern-making resources (e.g., blocks to trace)
- scissors
- paper and colored pencils
- glue
- pattern blocks (page 30)
- hand cut-outs (page 31)
- What's My Pattern? worksheet (page 32)

Directions
- Ask students, "What is a pattern? What is not a pattern? Where do you find patterns? Why?" (e.g., for decoration on dress material, wallpaper, floor tiles)
- Ask students, "How can you make a pattern?" (e.g., Trace blocks on paper strips to make a long line of shapes.)

color   ⚪⚫⚫⚪⚫⚫   number ⣿⣀⣿⣀⣿⣀

size   ⚪○⚪○⚪○   shape ○○□○○□○○□

position ○○○○○○○

- Form small groups. Each group selects a pattern type to explore together. (e.g., color, position, number)

Variations
- Copy the pattern blocks onto colored paper (e.g., blue, green, yellow, red). Have students cut them out and rearrange them to make patterns. Have students record their patterns by gluing them onto paper.
- Students cut out the hands. They use one of the hands to hide part of their pattern while a friend predicts the hidden shapes.
- Students use the What's My Pattern? worksheet to create their own instructions for drawing shape patterns on the truck trailers, can labels, and the kite tail.

29

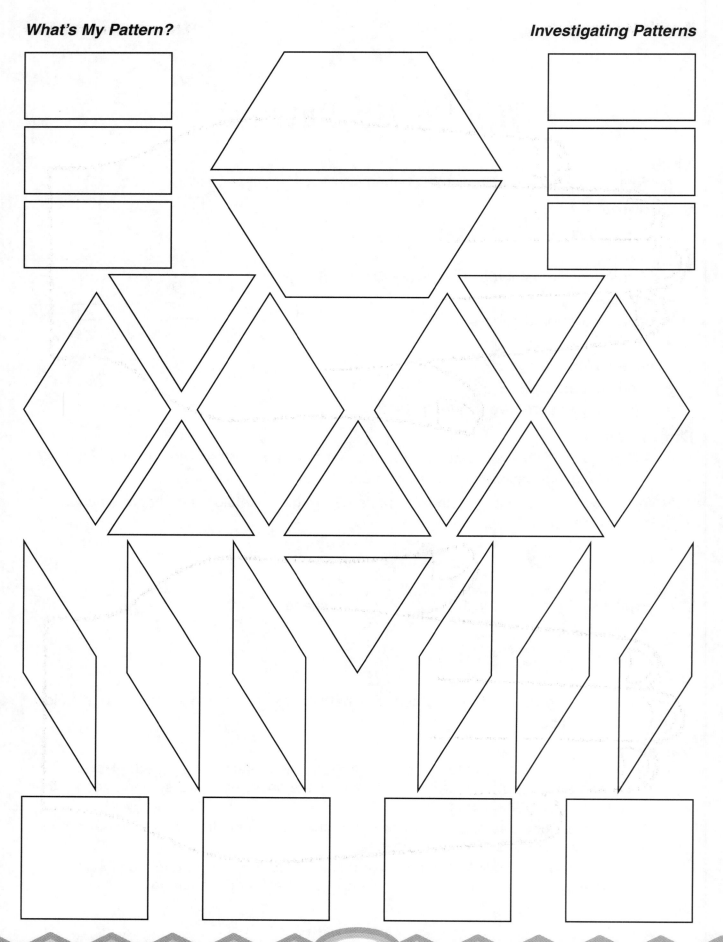

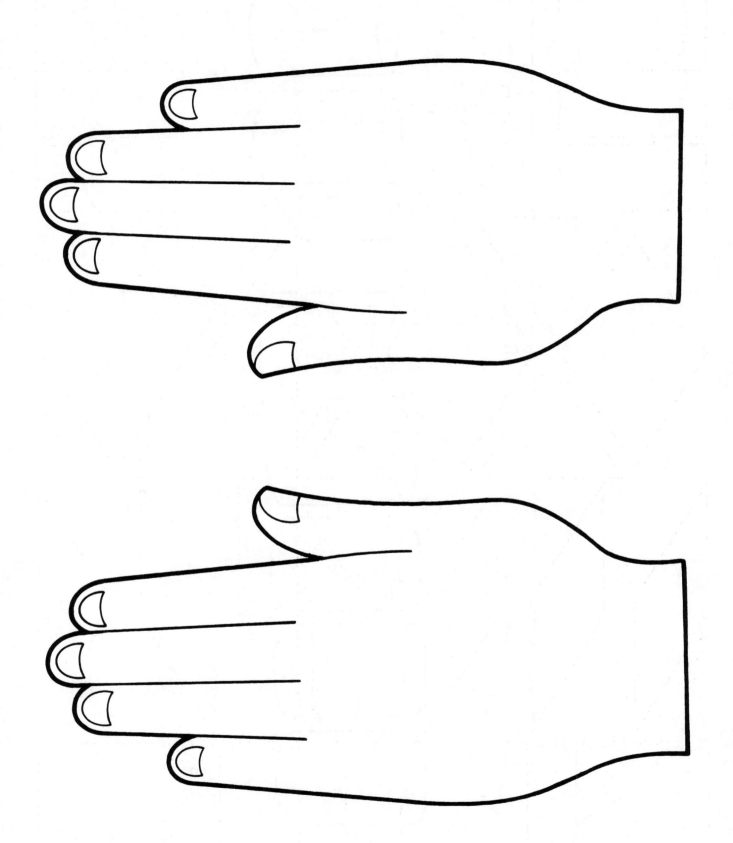

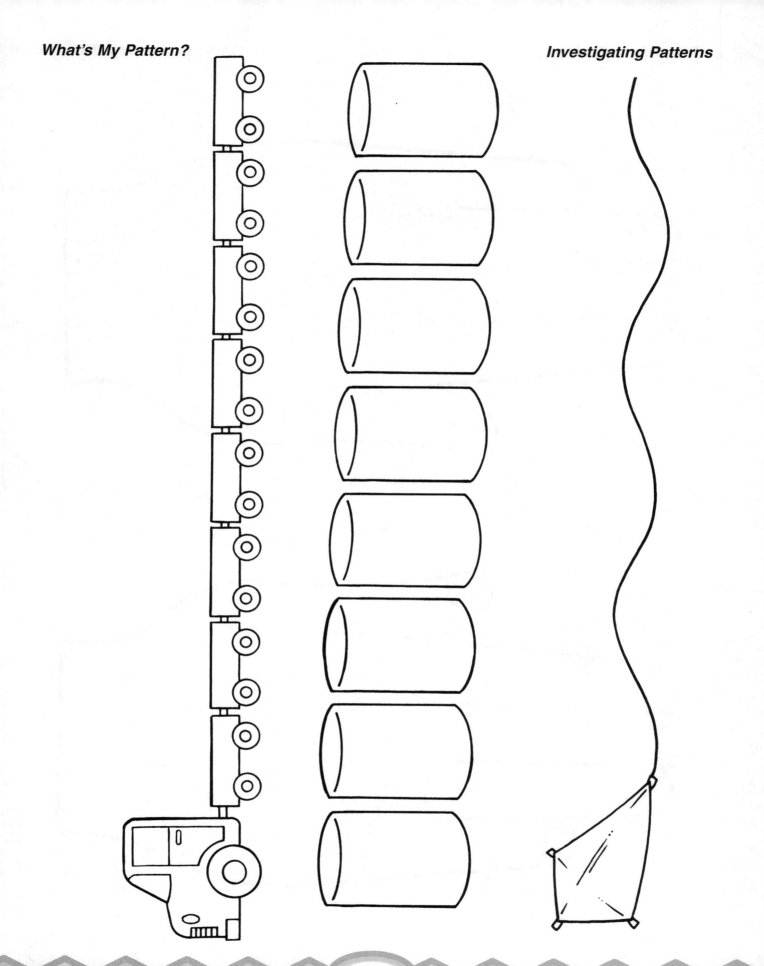

Flip It

Skill
- Flip, slide, and turn 2-D shapes to construct patterns

Grouping
- whole class
- pairs

Materials
- variety of flat shapes (e.g., tiles, attribute blocks)
- a large mirror (for teacher use only)
- safety mirrors (e.g., silver cardboard)
- paper and pencils
- Flip It worksheet (page 34)
- Flip It copy cards (page 35)

Directions
- Hold up a mirror. Ask, "What happens when you look at yourself in a mirror?" (e.g., You see your reflection.) Explain that a reflection is a mirror image of something and another name for this is a *flip*.
- Have students use a safety mirror with a partner to investigate flips. Students place their mirrors on objects around the room and look at the reflections. They should notice how the whole shape changes depending on where they place their mirror. Tell students that each shape now has two identical halves.
- Ask, "How can you use flips to make patterns?" (e.g., Trace around a shape on paper, then flip the shape over and trace it again.)
- Ask, "In how many directions can you flip your shape?"

  Have students check their flip with a mirror between the two outlines. Ask, "Do you see the same pattern in your mirror?" Have them continue their pattern by making a long line of flips.
- Have students make a design using two or more tiles. Have them make their flip pattern by making a mirror image of this design with more tiles.

Variations
- Students use a safety mirror to investigate the reflections of creatures on the Flip It worksheet.
- Students use the pattern blocks (page 30) or mosaic tiles (page 41) to copy and continue the patterns on the Flip It copy cards.

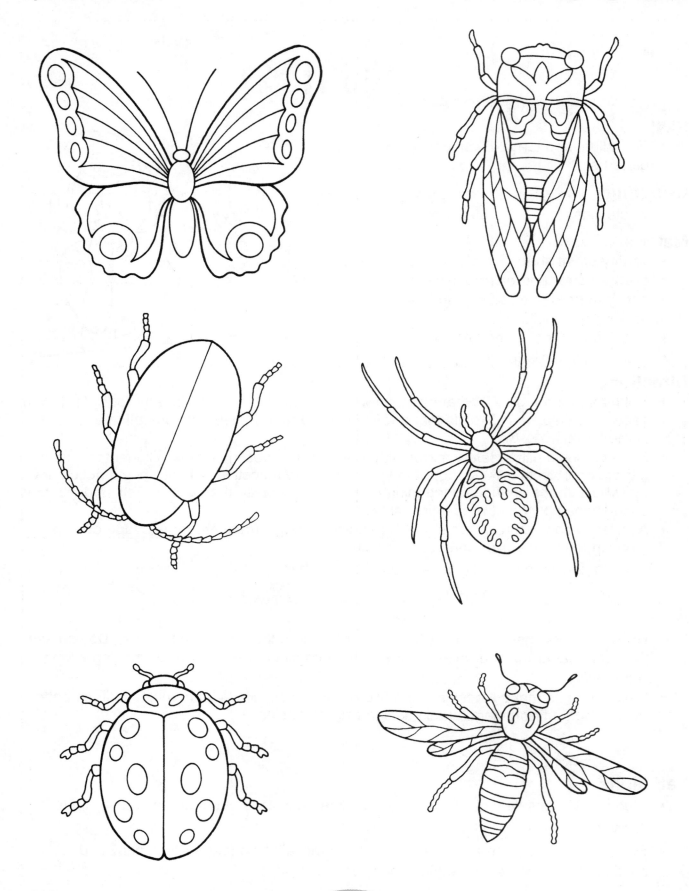

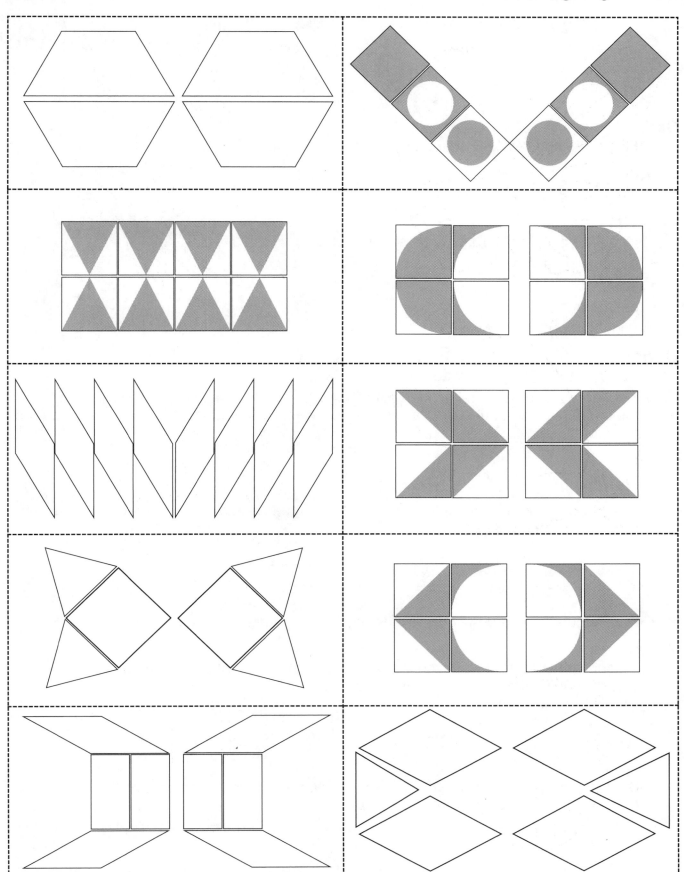

#3531 Math in Action

Slide It

Skill

- Flip, slide, and turn 2-D shapes to construct patterns

Grouping

- whole class
- pairs

Materials

- variety of flat shapes (e.g., tiles, attribute blocks)
- paper and pencils
- scissors
- cardboard
- Slide It copy cards (page 37)

Directions

- Ask students, "What's a slide?"
- Hold up a 2-D shape. Tell students that when you slide a shape, you keep it facing in the same direction, but slide it anywhere you want it. It does not flip itself over to create a mirror image.

- Ask students, "How many different ways could you create a repeating slide pattern with tiles of the same shape?"

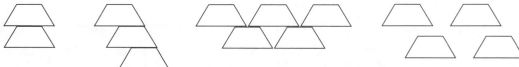

- Have students record their discoveries by tracing or drawing their patterns on paper.

Variations

- Students cut out an unusual shape from cardboard and explore different ways to slide and trace this new shape to create slide patterns.

- Students copy and continue the Slide It copy card patterns using pattern blocks (page 30) or they create some of their own.
- Students copy and continue the Slide It copy card patterns using mosaic tiles (page 41) or they create some of their own.

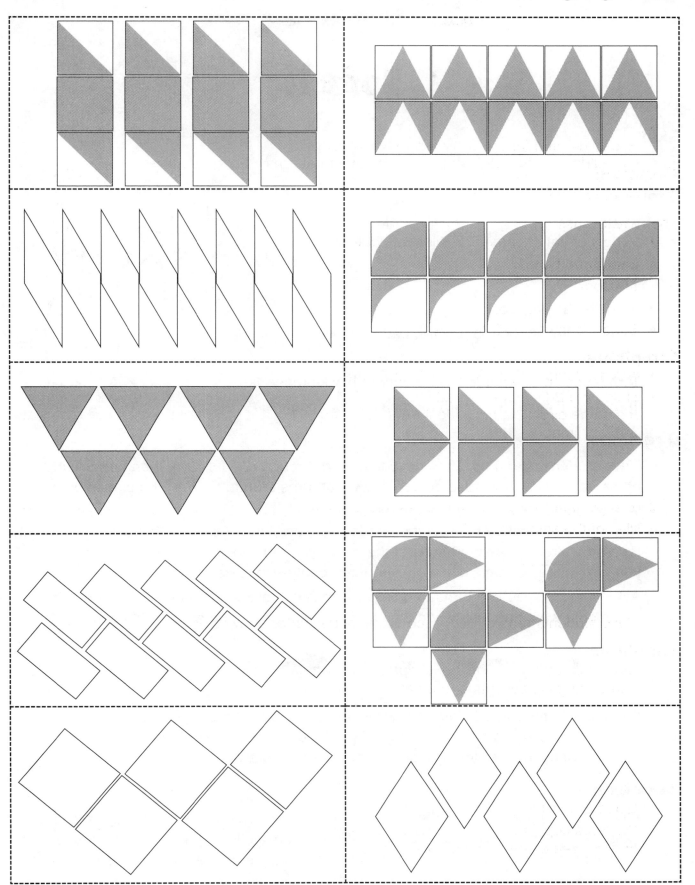

Turn It

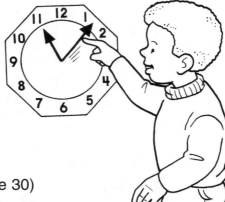

Skill

- Flip, slide, and turn 2-D shapes to construct patterns

Grouping

- whole class
- pairs

Materials

- a geared analog clock
- variety of flat shapes (e.g., tiles, pattern blocks)
- paper and pencils
- Turn It copy cards (page 39) for pattern blocks (page 30)
- Turn It copy cards (page 40) for mosaic tiles (page 41)

Directions

- Have students stand up. Then have them turn around one full turn, then turn around the other way. Ask, "What else do you know that turns around?" (e.g., the blades on a fan or a windmill, the wheels on a bicycle)

- Have students look at the way the hands of a clock turn. Tell them that when you turn in the same direction as the hands of the clock, you turn clockwise. Tell them that when you turn in the opposite direction, you turn counter-clockwise.

- Ask, "How can you use turns to create patterns?" Have students take a shape and investigate what happens when they turn it clockwise around a point or a corner.

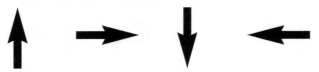

- Form small groups, each with a different pattern-making resource—pattern blocks, bathroom tiles, mosaic tiles, or tiles. Have students explore ways to create turning patterns with multiple tiles by placement, tracing, or drawing.

Variations

- Students copy and continue the Turn It copy card patterns (page 39) and pattern blocks (page 30) and/or the Copy Cards (page 40) and mosaic tiles (page 41). Reproduce the Copy Cards at 200% for 1-1 matching, or have students create some of their own.

Copy Cards for Pattern Blocks

Copy Cards for Mosaic Tiles

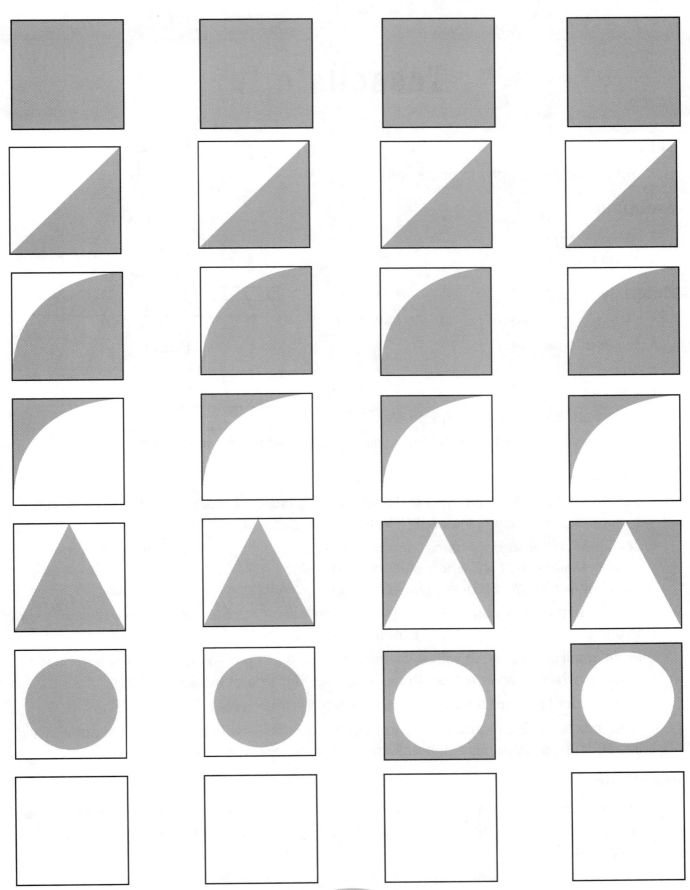

Tessellate It

Skill

- Tessellate 2-D shapes to make patterns

Grouping

- whole class
- small groups

Materials

- pictures or posters of real-life tile patterns
- paper and pencils
- glue
- scissors
- Tessellate It pattern cards (page 43)
- plastic/wooden/foam pattern blocks, tiles, pattern blocks (page 30)

Directions

- Ask students, "Where can you find tiles covering large surfaces?" Students investigate picture or poster examples. Ask, "What shapes can you see?"
- Tell students the special name for patterns made by fitting tiles together with no gaps or overlaps is *tessellation*. Show students some tiles. Ask, "Which of these tiles will fit together like that?" Students guess, then check. Ask, "Do all tiles tessellate?"
- Ask students, "How can you record your discoveries?" (e.g., Trace or draw tiles on paper to make a tessellation.) Demonstrate some strategies.
- Form small groups, each with a different pattern-making resource. Challenge groups to discover which shapes tessellate by fitting together tiles of the same shape.
- Have students record their discoveries and compare results.
- Next, challenge each group to make patterns using tiles with two different shapes. Try three-, four-, or five-shape patterns, depending on ability or interest levels.

Variations

- Students use the Tessallate It pattern cards as examples which combine two, three, four, or five different tile shapes. Copy at 200% for 1-1 matching with the pattern blocks (page 30).
- Students make their own tile pattern cards to challenge other teams.

Exploring Symmetry

In this unit, students will do the following:

- Identify matching halves in a 2-D shape
- Identify lines of symmetry in a 2-D shape
- Identify, make, and continue symmetrical patterns

(For skills used in this section, refer to the Skills Record Sheet on page 95.)

Hunting Halves

Skills

- Identify matching halves in a 2-D shape
- Identify lines of symmetry in a 2-D shape

Grouping

- whole class

Materials

- a pile of clothes
- glue
- string
- scissors
- safety mirrors (e.g., silver cardboard)
- workbooks or paper for recording
- Hunting Halves cards (page 46)

Directions

- Have students stand and face a partner. Ask, "Where can you see matching halves?" (e.g., my friend's face—the left half looks the same as the right half.) Discuss the word *symmetrical*. Demonstrate how to see the matching half in a mirror.
- Hold up a shirt. Ask students, "How can you find matching halves on this shirt?" (e.g., Fold it in half down the center.) Demonstrate with other clothes. Ask, "Why are clothes made this way?"
- Have students imagine if people were not symmetrical. Ask, "What might they look like? Is the top half of a person the same as the bottom half?"
- Ask, "Where else can you see matching halves around you?" Have students find something that has matching halves in more than one way. (e.g., school lunch box—the left and right match.)
- Discuss lines of symmetry. (e.g., These are the imaginary fold lines that show where two halves meet. If you place a mirror along one of these lines, you see the matching shape reflected.) Demonstrate how to place string along a fold line to show the line of symmetry on a shape. Check using a mirror.
- Have students go on a Halves Hunt with a partner. Have them use string and a mirror to identify lines of symmetry and draw pictures of some of the shapes they discover.

Variations

- Students cut out and match the Hunting Halves cards to create five symmetrical pictures.
- Students play Match My Face. Students cut out a large face from a magazine. Then they fold and cut it in half and glue one half onto paper. A partner must draw in the matching half.

45

#3531 Math in Action   ©Teacher Created Resources, Inc.

Make My Other Half

Skills
- Identify matching halves in a 2-D shape
- Identify lines of symmetry in a 2-D shape

Grouping
- whole class
- small groups

Materials
- cookies
- painting equipment
- colored paper squares
- Flip It worksheet (page 34)
- Make My Other Half worksheet (page 48)
- scissors
- colored pencils
- pencils and paper
- glue

Directions
- Pass around some cookies. Ask students, "Can you break them into matching halves? Can you eat one so that only half remains? Can you make half of one-half? What are different ways you can make matching halves?" (e.g., Close and open your hands.)

- Form four small groups for rotating activities. Collect the equipment they need.

  1. **Paint It:** Have students fold a piece of paper in half. Have them place blobs of paint inside one half. Tell them to close their paper, squash it flat, and open it out to dry. Tell them to create a symmetrical creature by adding extra features. (e.g., ears, eyes, legs)

  2. **Cut It:** Have students fold pieces of paper in half. Tell them to imagine what half a person, or a cat, or a house looks like. Have students cut out the shape they think will open out to create the whole picture.

  3. **Draw It:** Have students look at the five pictures on the Make My Other Half worksheet. Have them draw in the matching halves.

  4. **Draw It:** Have students use the Flip It worksheet with a partner. Have students cut the six creatures in half along the line of symmetry. Then have them share the halves between them. Have them glue one half of each creature onto their papers and draw in the matching half.

Variations
- Students play *Mirror Me*. Students face a partner and match every move they make, as if they are a reflection in a mirror.
- Students share the Hunting Halves cards (page 46) with a friend. Students glue each half onto their papers and draw the missing half.

47

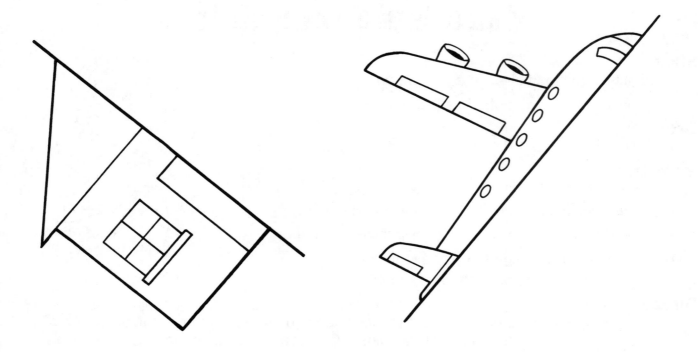

Match My Design

Skill
- Identify, make, and continue symmetrical patterns

Grouping
- small groups

Materials
- pattern blocks (e.g., page 30)
- mosaic tiles (e.g., page 41)
- safety mirrors (e.g., silver cardboard)
- Match My Design copy cards (pages 50 and 51)

Directions
- Tell students that making a symmetrical pattern with tiles is easy. Tell them to make any design using two or more tiles. Have them decide where they would like the line of symmetry to be. Tell them to repeat their design by flipping it along this line of symmetry.

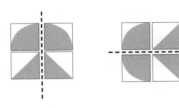

- Have students work with a partner, using mosaic tiles or pattern blocks. Tell them one person makes a tile design and states where they would like the line of symmetry to be. The other player repeats the design as a flip along the symmetry line. If there are enough tiles, have them continue their pattern to make a line of flips.

- Have students play Symmetry Challenge. Have them make a design from tiles and then show it to their partner for a short time. (e.g., 5–10 seconds, telling them where they want the line of symmetry to be) Students hide their design, then challenge their partner to make an exact copy that is flipped along the line of symmetry.

Variations
- Students create a tile pattern that flips in two ways. (e.g., from left to right, from top to bottom.)
- Students use Match My Design copy cards on pages 50 and 51 to make and continue symmetrical patterns. Enlarge 200% for 1-1 matching. Ask, "Which patterns are double flips?"

Investigating Solid Properties

In this unit, students will do the following:

- Identify, count, and describe faces, edges, and corners of 3-D objects

(For skills used in this section, refer to the Skills Record Sheet on page 95.)

What Shape Is My Face?

Skill
- Identify, count, and describe faces, edges, and corners of 3-D objects

Grouping
- whole class
- pairs

Materials
- close-up pictures of wild animals *(optional)*
- paint
- a collection of interesting 3-D objects
- geometric blocks
- paper
- dot stickers
- What Shape Is My Face? worksheet (page 54)

Directions
- Ask students to close their eyes. Tell them to imagine the face of a wild animal. Ask, "What does it look like?" Tell them to open their eyes and tell the person sitting next to them what they saw.
- Ask students, "What is a face? Do all people have faces? Do all animals?"
- Pass around some 3-D objects. Ask students, "Do objects have faces? How can you tell?" Discuss different reactions.
- Explain that a face on an object is not like a face on a person or an animal. It is a flat surface. Tell them not all objects will have faces whereas some objects can have many faces, unlike people and animals. The faces also feel different. (e.g., Some may be smooth. Some may feel rough.)
- Find an object with a flat face. (e.g., a box) Ask, "What shape is this face? Can you find a different object with the same face shape as this one?"
- Have students find a partner. Have them walk around the room together. Tell them to find faces that are the shape of a square, a circle, a triangle, or a rectangle. Ask, "Are there any other face shapes you can discover?"
- Tell students to record their favorite discoveries on the worksheet.

Variations
- Students count the number of faces on an object and put a dot sticker on each face to show it has been counted. Ask, "Which object has the most faces?"
- Students identify different faces on blocks and paint the faces in different colors or print face patterns on paper.

Where's My Edge?

Skill

- Identify, count, and describe faces, edges, and corners of 3-D objects

Grouping

- whole class
- pairs

Materials

- a collection of 3-D objects
- one-minute timer
- Where's My Edge? cards (page 56)

Directions

- Have students close their eyes. Have them imagine they are at a swimming pool and are standing right on the edge.

- Ask students, "What is an edge? Where do you see edges?" (e.g., the edge of a cliff, the edge of a forest, the edge of the playground)

- Explain to students that the edge of an object is where two faces meet. Pass around some objects to explore with their hands. Ask, "Do all objects have an edge? Can an object have more than one edge?" Discuss their discoveries. (e.g., An edge can be very long. An edge can be sharp or soft.)

- Consider safety issues. Explain that some edges are so sharp they can cut you. Remind them to take care when exploring edges with their fingers.

- With a partner, have students walk around inside and outside the classroom investigating edges.

- Discuss their discoveries after a suitable time limit.

Variation

- Students work in small groups. Tell them to shuffle the Where's My Edge? cards and give one to each player. Start a one-minute timer. Students try to find a matching shape to bring back to their group within the time limit.

**the shortest
edge**

**the longest
edge**

**the most
edges**

**the fewest
edges**

**a soft
edge**

**a sharp
edge**

**a wiggly
edge**

**the most
interesting
edge**

**all curved
edges**

**all straight
edges**

Corners

Skill

- Identify, count, and describe faces, edges, and corners of 3-D objects

Grouping

- whole class
- pairs

Materials

- one-minute timer
- scissors
- a very large cardboard box
- glue
- colored pencils
- Little Jack Horner cut-outs (pages 58 and 59)
- prepared example of Little Jack Horner

Directions

- Have students recite the rhyme "Little Jack Horner." Ask everyone to stand up and move to a corner of the room like Jack. Ask, "How do you know where this is? What is a corner?" Discuss everyone's suggestions.

- Tell students a *corner* is the point or place where three or more faces on an object meet. It can be sharp to touch. There can be corners on the inside of objects (e.g., a room) or the outside of objects. Tell them the corner of the room is the spot where the two walls and the floor (or ceiling) meet. It is only a tiny place, just large enough to put their finger tip into, but the word usually refers to the whole area near this.

- Discuss the inside and outside corners of the box.

- Start the timer. Ask, "How many different corners can you spot by the time one minute is up? What is the highest corner you can see? The lowest corner? The tiniest corner? The sharpest corner? Are there any other inside corners you can discover? Which object has the most corners?"

- Show students your prepared example of Little Jack Horner and his corner. Demonstrate how to cut out his room on the heavy lines then fold on the dashed lines to create the corner. Students can use tape to secure their corners. Show how to cut Jack out along the heavy lines (do not forget to cut along the inside of his arms) and fold on the dashed lines. Students can cut out the pie and glue or tape it to Jack's right hand, then place him in his corner.

Variations

- Students draw their own picture of Little Jack Horner to color, cut out, and place in a corner of their home.
- Students look for other poems, rhymes, and stories about corners or write their own.

Cut along thick, solid lines and then fold along dashed lines.

Cut along thick, solid lines and then fold along dashed lines.

#3531 Math in Action

Constructing and Modeling

In this unit, students will do the following:

- Construct 2-D shapes through body movements and games
- Construct 2-D shapes using sticks
- Construct and model 3-D objects using a variety of materials

(For skills used in this section, refer to the Skills Record Sheet on page 95.)

Body Shapes

Skill
- Construct 2-D shapes through body movements and games

Grouping
- pairs
- small groups
- whole class

Materials
- long ropes
- glue
- a whistle
- scissors
- Body Shapes pictures (page 62)
- large sheets of paper
- a leader to call out shape names at random

Directions
- Have students play Body Shapes with a partner. On a signal, the leader calls out a shape. Students try to find at least two ways to make that shape using their hands.

rectangle triangle

- Repeat, but this time tell them to use their whole body, with or without their partner, to create the shape.

 triangle

- Have students play Body Shapes Challenge on the playground or in a large open hall. Tell them to walk around clockwise and then on a signal (e.g., a whistle), the leader calls out a number between two and six. Students race to form small groups with the matching number of people. The leader then calls out a shape. Each group works cooperatively to make that shape with their bodies. Ask students, "What is the largest shape you can make together? What is the largest number of shapes you can make in your group each time?"

- Repeat, but this time each person in the group holds a length of rope between them to create the required shape. Each body might be a corner of the shape.

Variation
- Students cut out the Body Shapes pictures. They use these to record shapes made by bodies holding a rope. Students glue each person into position and then glue colored wool or string or draw a line between them showing how the shape is formed.

Sticks

Skill
- Construct 2-D shapes using sticks

Grouping
- whole class   • small groups

Materials
- one-minute timers
- pencils and paper
- play clay
- Sticks activity cards (page 64)
- Sticks spinners copied onto cardstock, cut out, with a pencil with a paper clip through the center (page 65)
- geoboards and rubberbands
- glue
- Sticks Puzzles (page 66)
- sticks (e.g., toothpicks, straws, craft sticks)

Directions
- Ask three people to lie on the floor and make a triangle with their bodies. Ask, "Can six people work as a team to construct a body triangle? Can nine? Can 12?"
- Demonstrate how to use sticks as a substitute for people's bodies in making shapes.

- Tell them that if the sides are all the same and the corners are all the same, it is a regular shape.

- Tell them that if the sides are different, or the corners are different, it is an irregular shape.

- Have students form four small groups with one activity card and a different type of stick for each group. Encourage each group to record their favorite shapes by drawing, cutting paper strips, or gluing sticks directly onto paper.
- Have the fast workers try the Sticks Puzzles (page 66). Each puzzle has three different problems.

Variations
- Students construct shapes by placing stick ends into play clay balls, or even marshmallows.
- Students investigate stick shapes by observing the framework of buildings under construction. (e.g., use posters or pictures)

Seeing Stars

- How many different ways can you construct a star from sticks?
- What is the smallest number of sticks you need?
- How many arms are on each star?

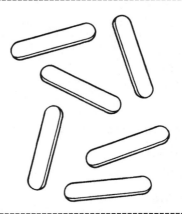

Amazing Arrows

- How many different ways can you construct an arrow shape from sticks?
- What is the smallest number of sticks you need?
- Draw your favorite shape.

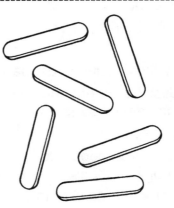

Shape Shuffle

- Use the one-minute timer and a spinner.
- Spin the spinner construct a shape using the matching number of sticks.
- How many different shapes can you construct from these sticks in one minute?
- Are they regular or irregular?

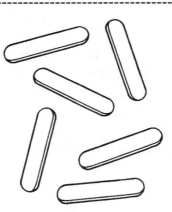

Geoboards

- Use the one-minute timer and a spinner.
- Spin the spinner and construct a shape using the geoboard.
- How many different shapes can you discover in one minute?

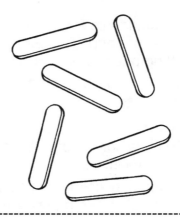

#3531 Math in Action ©*Teacher Created Resources, Inc.*

Spinner Directions

Color and cut out the spinner. Put a paper clip over the tip of a pencil. Place the tip of the pencil on the center of the spinner and spin the paper clip.

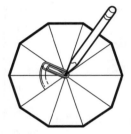

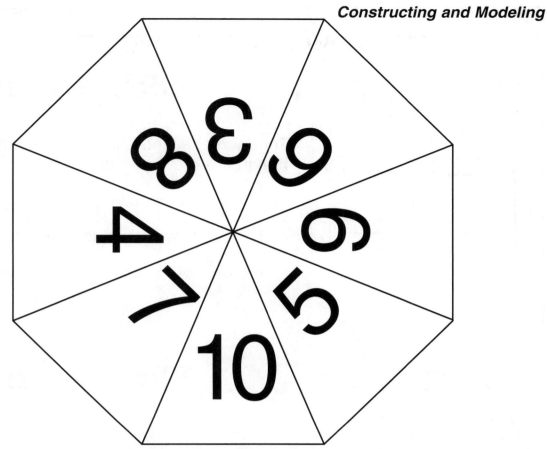

Spinner Directions

Color and cut out the spinner. Put a paper clip over the tip of a pencil. Place the tip of the pencil on the center of the spinner and spin the paper clip.

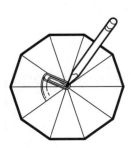

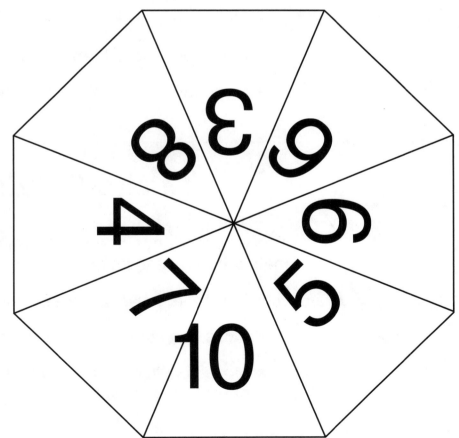

     #3531 Math in Action

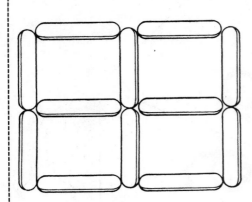

Sticks Puzzles

Try each challenge, then replace the sticks to match the drawing before trying the next.

- Remove two sticks leaving only two squares.

- Move three sticks to make three squares.

- Move four sticks to make 10 squares.

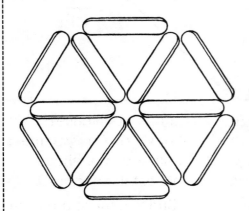

Sticks Puzzles

Try each challenge, then replace the sticks to match the drawing before trying the next.

- Move three sticks to make four triangles.

- Move four sticks to make five diamonds.

- Move four sticks to make three trapezoids.

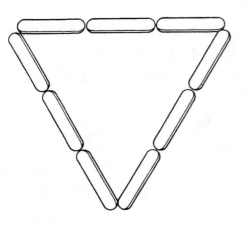

Sticks Puzzles

Try each challenge, then replace the sticks to match the drawing before trying the next.

- Move three sticks to make three triangles.

- Move five sticks to make five triangles.

- Move six sticks to make three diamonds and one hexagon.

#3531 Math in Action

What Shape Is It?

Skill
- Construct and model 3-D objects using a variety of materials

Grouping
- up to four small groups

Materials
- a box of geometric-shaped cookies and a cookie tray
- paper and pencils
- parent helpers
- play clay
- sliced bread, cookie cutters, plastic knives, jelly
- bubble mix and bubble blowers, soft wire
- What Shape Is It? activity cards (pages 68 and 69)

Directions
- Tip out the cookies onto a tray. Ask, "How can you make a 3-D shape from these?" (e.g., stacking them to create a tall shape) Ask, "Is there any other way? Can you make a cylinder or a box shape? Is your shape solid or hollow? What other cookie-shape challenges can you think of?" After your discussion, have students eat the cookies.
- Blow some bubbles. Talk about the shapes students see. Ask, "Can you make a bubble like a box? A ball? A cylinder? Why? Why not? Is a bubble solid or hollow? Can a bubble have a hole in it? What other bubble challenges can you think of?"
- Form rotating groups with a parent helper and an activity card for each group. Give each group the following materials:

    Squish It: play clay   *Cut It:* sliced bread, cookie cutters, plastic knives, jelly

    Mold It: play clay   *Blow It:* bubble mix, bubble blowers, soft wire

    Explain the group tasks. Tell students to try to create as many different 3-D shapes as they can with their materials.
- Discuss the results of their explorations together. Have students record their best discoveries on paper.

Variation
- Students try making different shapes with wet sand in a sand tray. Use plastic molds, homemade molds, or just bare hands.

Squish It

Secretly make an object.

Exchange it with a friend and then talk about your new shape.

Guess what it is.

If you are correct, squish it and start again.

If not, ask your partner to keep adding bits until you guess correctly.

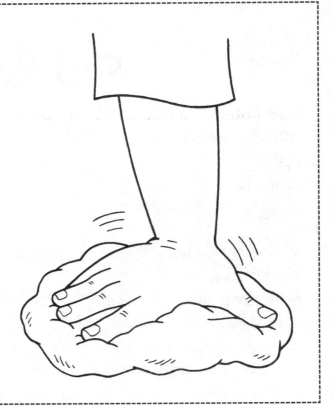

Mold It

Make a shape from play clay.

What's the largest shape you can make?

What's the smallest?

Does your shape have faces, edges, or corners?

Can you make a shape with a hole in it?

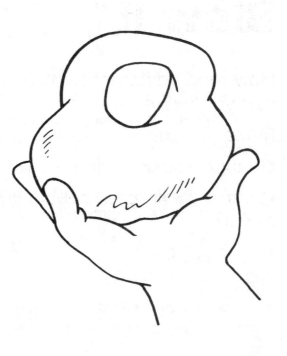

Cut It

Use cookie cutters to cut shapes from bread slices.

Which shapes have edges? Which have corners? Are there any that have no corners?

Use a plastic knife to cut your own shapes from bread slices.

Make two identical shapes. Spread with jelly and have a snack!

Blow It

How many different bubble shapes can you make?

Make your own blowers.

Change your bubble mix.

What is the largest bubble you can make?

Which bubble shape lasts the longest?

Exploring Position Language

In this unit, students will do the following:

- Use informal position language
- Describe the position of an object from different points of view
- Use the terms *left* and *right*
- Describe and follow simple directions

(For skills used in this section, refer to the Skills Record Sheet on page 95.)

Where Am I?

Skills

- Use informal position language
- Describe the position of an object from different points of view

Grouping

- whole class
- pairs

Materials

- toy collections (e.g., farm animals, wild animals, dinosaurs, small cars)
- teddy bear
- Where Is Baby? cards (page 72)

Directions

- **Where Am I?**

  Have a student describe his or her position in the room. (e.g., beside the table, near the window) Then, repeat with someone else in the room.

- **Who Am I?**

  Select five or more students to stand at random while the others keep their eyes closed. Ask students to guess who the standing ones are without mentioning their names. (e.g., They cannot ask, "Are you Phil?") Instead, they should ask position questions. (e.g., "Are you in front of Lucy?" "Are you beside the cupboard?") Only when they have worked out all the clues can they say the name. Ask students, "How many questions were asked before the class guessed who you are?" Make a list showing all the position terms they used. (e.g., on the chalkboard or wall display) Discuss.

- **What Am I?**

  Form pairs. Give each pair five or more objects. (e.g., farm animals) Rearrange these objects in front of them. Tell students to secretly imagine they are one of the objects. Their partners ask position questions to guess which one they are. Have students keep a record of how many questions they ask. Ask, "What is the fewest number of questions you need?"

Variations

- Students play Where Is Teddy? Select someone to hide a teddy somewhere in the room, while everyone else shuts their eyes. Students can ask position questions to discover teddy's secret hiding place. (e.g., Is the teddy bear inside the cupboard?)

- Students play Where Is Baby? Tell students that Baby loves to play games with her father. Shuffle the cards. Students take turns looking at the top card. Describe Baby's position by inventing a small story. (e.g., Baby is hiding behind Dad because she is frightened of the rhino at the zoo.)

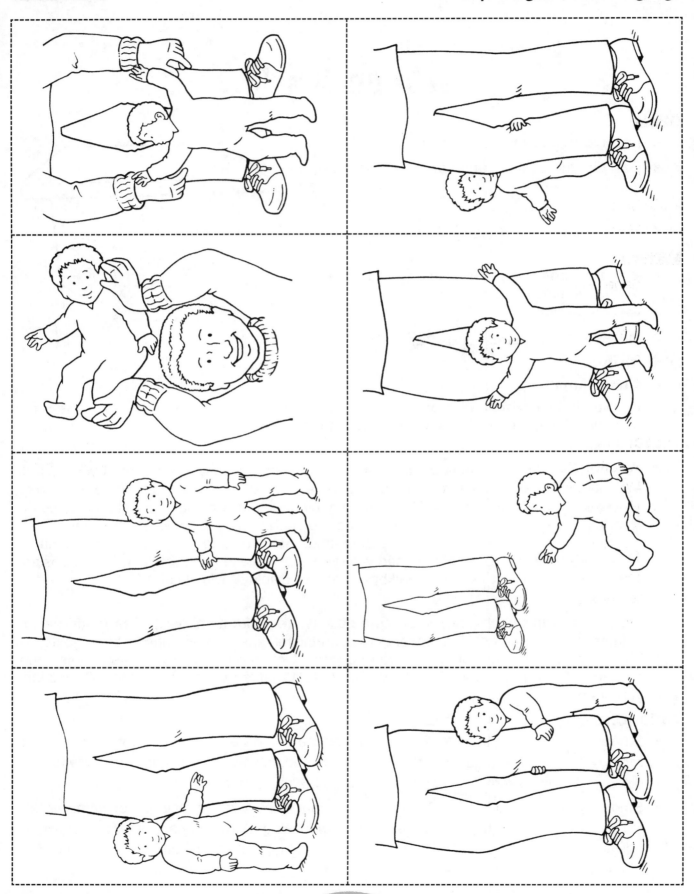

Line Them Up

Skills

- Use informal position language
- Describe the position of an object from different points of view

Grouping

- whole class
- pairs

Materials

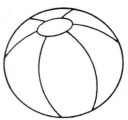

- paper, cut into two long strips
- pencils
- crayons
- scissors
- glue
- Line Them Up worksheet (page 74)

Directions

- Ask five students to stand in a line at the front of the class. Ask students, "Who is first? Who is last? Who is next to Sam?"
- Play Who Am I? with the students. Secretly select a student and give position clues. Ask, "How quickly can someone guess which person I am thinking of?"
- Discuss the objects on the worksheet. Have students color and cut them out. Have them tell a partner how to glue objects in a line by giving position clues. (e.g., "The emu is first. The apple is next to the emu.")
- Exchange strips with another pair. Play Who Am I? Ask students, "Can you quickly guess which object your partner is thinking of by asking position questions?"
- Review different ways to describe a position.

Variations

- Students glue their objects anywhere on a whole page and play Who Am I? with a partner.
- Students play Where Are You? with a partner or as a whole class game. On the playground, someone calls out instructions for everyone to follow. (e.g., "Go around the large tree and under the monkey bars.") He or she then calls out "Where are you now?" Someone else calls out his or her position. (e.g., "I am beside the wall. "I am next to the fence.")

Left or Right?

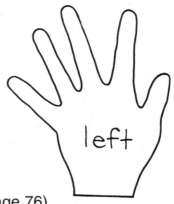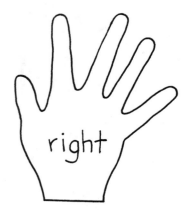

Skills
- Describe the position of an object from different points of view
- Use the terms *left* and *right*

Grouping
- whole class

Materials
- paper
- scissors
- ribbons
- crayons
- glue
- foot cut-outs (page 76)
- hand cut-outs (page 31)

Directions
- Have students look at their hands. Talk about the similarities and differences. (e.g., Older hands are more wrinkled. Some hands might have freckles.) Have students look at the shape of their hands. (e.g., fingers held together, fingers spread apart)
- Have students trace the outline of their hands onto paper. Ask students, "Whose hand is the largest? The smallest? How can you tell?" (e.g., Compare by overlapping hands onto the outline.)
- Discuss the fact that some people use their left hand more than their right. Find out who is left-handed in the class. Tie a ribbon around everyone's left hand. Investigate what their left hand looks like when it is face down on the desk or face up. Ask students, "Where is the thumb each time?"
- Have students write the word *left* on their left-hand outline.
- Have students explore what they can do with their left hand. (e.g., "Can you write your name? Throw a ball? Undo a shirt button?")
- Have students make a list of things that are easy to do with their left hand and things that are difficult to do.

Variations
- Have a "Left Day." (e.g., Walk starting with their left foot. Try to do everything they can with their left hand. Eat their lunch chewing everything from the left side.)
- Make multiple copies of the foot outlines. Have students color them. (e.g., left foot red, right foot green) Laminate *(optional)* and have students cut them out. Students shuffle the cutouts and place these in a long line all around the room. Ask someone to walk along it following the left or right instructions. (e.g., "Left, left, left" means hop three times on the left foot.)

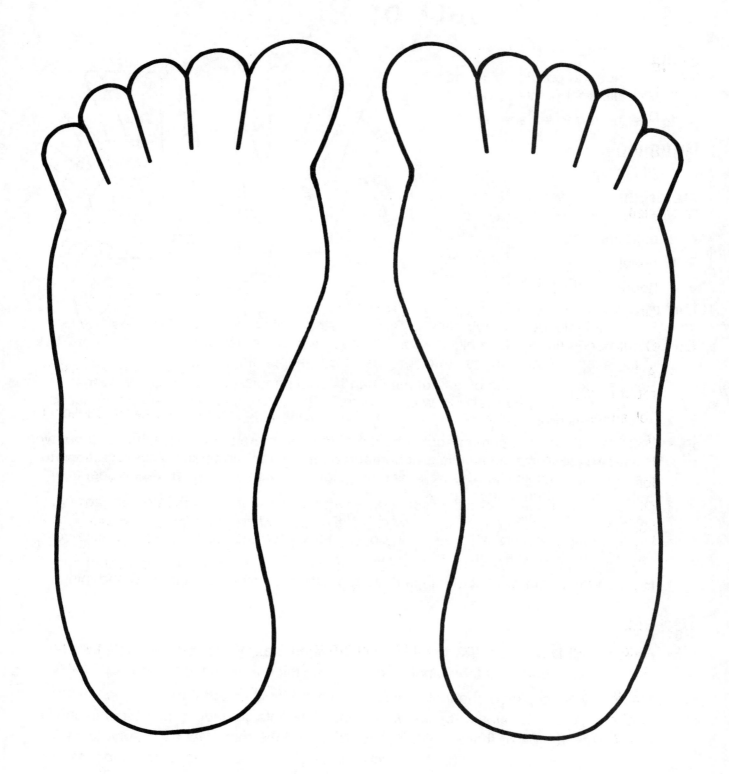

#3531 Math in Action

Robots

Skills

- Use the terms *left* and *right*
- Describe and follow simple directions

Grouping

- whole class
- pairs

Materials

- balls
- beanbags
- hoops
- direction spinner and activity cards (page 78)

Directions

- Ask students, "What is a robot? Why did humans invent them? What would you ask a robot to do if you had one for a day?"
- Tell students to imagine they are robots. Ask, "What directions will you need to follow to move to the door?" (e.g., Go forward four steps. Turn right.)
- Have students form pairs. One person is a robot. The other person gives directions to follow. Have them exchange roles after a suitable time limit. (e.g., three minutes)
- Discuss any problems or difficulties. (e.g., Left and right relate to the person moving. If you and your robot are both facing forward, then left and right will mean the same. If your robot is facing you, then their left and right will be opposite to yours. You can solve this problem by always facing in the same direction as your robot. Or your robot can wear a ribbon on their left hand as a reminder.)

Variation

- Students form small groups. Supply each group with a spinner, activity cards placed face down, a beanbag, a ball, and a hoop. Students take turns spinning the spinner, turning over the top card, and following the instructions. (e.g., Jump to the left. Catch a beanbag with your left hand. Bowl a hoop backward.)

  Ask students, "Are some instructions easier to carry out than others?"

#3531 Math in Action

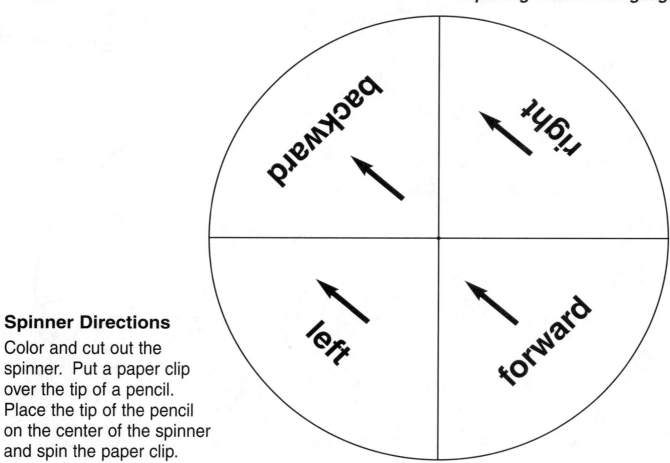

Spinner Directions

Color and cut out the spinner. Put a paper clip over the tip of a pencil. Place the tip of the pencil on the center of the spinner and spin the paper clip.

kick a ball	bowl a hoop
catch a beanbag	throw a ball
hop	jump

Identifying Positions

In this unit, students will do the following:

- Describe the position of an object in models, pictures, and sketches
- Construct a model from memory, verbal instructions, or diagrams
- Draw an object from different points of view

(For skills used in this section, refer to the Skills Record Sheet on page 95.)

Dinosaur Bones

Skills

- Describe the position of an object in models, pictures, and sketches
- Construct a model from memory, verbal instructions, or diagrams

Grouping

- whole class
- pairs within four small groups

Materials

- model dinosaurs
- construction materials (e.g., wooden blocks, building blocks)
- a cloth (e.g., a dish towel)
- Dinosaur Bones activity cards (pages 81 and 82)

Directions

- Ask students, "What do you know about dinosaurs?"
- Ask students to imagine they are paleontologists hunting for dinosaur bones. Tell them that they have discovered a complete set, but the bones are jumbled up. Ask, "How will you put them back together?" Have students discuss with another paleontologist.
- Ask students to imagine the construction materials are dinosaur bones. Demonstrate how to build part of a dinosaur with four pieces. Ask, "What could this be?" (e.g., part of a dinosaur head or a leg)
- Form four groups with one activity card per group. Tell students to find a partner within their group. Have them collect two identical sets of 4–6 blocks, where the color, shape, and size match. Suggest that each pair start by using 3–4 blocks for each activity. Increase the difficulty later by adding one block at a time.

Variations

- **More Pieces**

  Students try using more pieces. Ask, "What is the largest number of pieces you can copy from memory? Is it easier to remember if all the pieces are the same color?"

- **Look Alikes**

  Students play as a group game with identical pieces for each player. The leader sits in the center with a model. The other players sit in a circle facing out. Each player asks the leader a question about the model. Ask, "What is the smallest number of questions needed to copy it?"

- **Talk to Me**

  Students take turns telling each other how to place one block at a time.

Yes/No

Sit back to back.

Secretly build a dinosaur.

Your partner tries to build an identical copy by asking you questions.

You can only answer "Yes" or "No."

Do not let your partner see your model until the end.

Compare models.

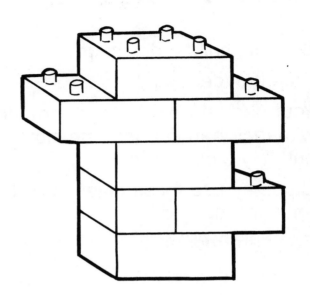

Look Alikes

Secretly build a dinosaur.

Show it to your partner for a short time; then hide it.

Ask your partner to make an identical copy from memory. How much time did he or she need?

Compare models.

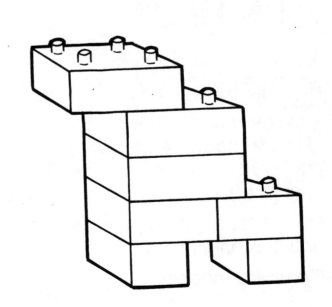

Under the Cloth

Secretly build a dinosaur.

Hide it under a cloth.

Your partner now feels your model with their hands under the cloth, but they cannot peek!

Can they use these clues to build an identical model?

Compare models.

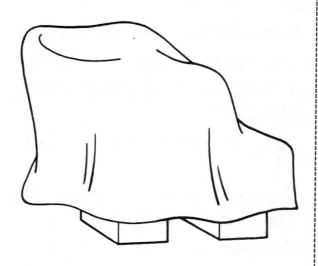

Talk to Me

Sit back to back.

Secretly build a dinosaur.

Tell your partner how to build an identical copy. (e.g., Put the large red piece next to the long blue one.)

Do not let them see your model until the end.

Compare models.

Draw Me

Skill

- Draw an object from different points of view

Grouping

- whole class
- small groups

Materials

- paper
- pencils
- blocks
- Draw Me cards (page 84)

Directions

- Have students stand up and face a partner. Talk about the different body parts they can see. (e.g., two arms, two hands, a neck)

- Discuss how to draw a picture of their partner. Ask, "Where will you start your drawing?" (e.g., At the head? At the feet? From one arm?)

- Discuss the position of each body part. (e.g., Your head is on top of your neck.) Ask, "What would you look like if the parts were in a different order?"

- Discuss the meaning of each instruction on the cards. (e.g., "Draw two legs" means without the feet. "Draw a head" means without any facial features.)

- Have students play a drawing game as a whole class or in small groups. Tell them to try to draw a complete body by drawing each part in isolation as instructed. Have students shuffle the cards. The leader calls out the instructions shown on the top card. Everyone draws that body part on their papers. Have students keep drawing one body part at a time until their person is complete. Have them compare drawings. Ask, "Are all the parts in the correct position? Are they all in proportion?"

Variations

- Students investigate famous works of art that mix up body parts. (e.g., Picasso's *Weeping Woman*)

- Pairs of students use two identical sets of blocks. They take turns building a model dinosaur with one set and drawing a picture of their model. Then they hide their model and ask their partner to use the second set of blocks to recreate an exact copy based on the drawing. Students compare models.

Draw a head.

Draw a body.

Draw two legs.

Draw two arms.

Draw two hands.

Draw two feet.

Draw some hair.

Draw two eyes.

Draw a mouth and a nose.

Draw a hat.

Exploring Paths and Grids

In this unit, students will do the following:

- Describe, follow, and draw a path on a simple map or maze
- Describe positions on a simple grid
- Use coordinates to describe positions on a simple grid

(For skills used in this section, refer to the Skills Record Sheet on page 95.)

Lead the Way

Skills

- Describe, follow, and draw a path on a simple map or maze

Grouping

- whole class
- pairs

Materials

- *Hansel and Gretel* storybook
- string
- wool
- colored chalk
- pencils and paper
- Lead the Way worksheet (page 87)

Directions

- Discuss animals that leave scent trails as they walk. (e.g., ants)
- Ask students, "When are your footsteps visible when you walk?" (e.g., after walking in a puddle of water, wet sand, or mud)
- Discuss the story of *Hansel and Gretel*, who left a breadcrumb trail into the forest.
- Ask students to imagine that everywhere they walk they leave a trail. Ask, "How could you do this?" (e.g., Tie string to your starting place or draw a chalk line behind you on the playground.)
- Have each student work with a partner. Have them decide on a way to mark a short trail in the room or on the playground. Ask another team to follow the trail. Ask, "Were there any problems?"
- Have students draw their trail on paper. Have them write about it, too!

Variations

- Students draw a map showing the way from their house to a friend's house. They show key things they see along the way and write instructions for someone else to follow.
- Students use the Lead the Way worksheet. Select two houses or landmarks. Students mark the path they would take to get from one to the other. Then, students write instructions for someone who is driving them from one place to the other.

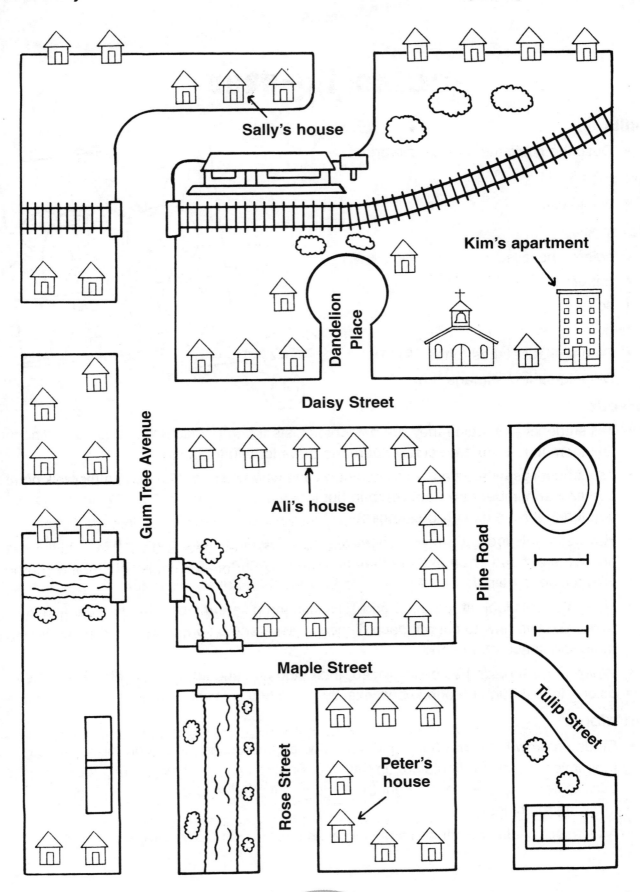

Sally's house

Kim's apartment

Dandelion Place

Daisy Street

Gum Tree Avenue

Ali's house

Pine Road

Maple Street

Rose Street

Tulip Street

Peter's house

#3531 Math in Action

Dino-jig-saur

Skills

- Describe positions on a simple grid

Grouping

- whole class   • pairs

Materials

- colored pencils
- paper
- scissors
- glue
- Dino-jig-saur pieces (page 89)
- Dino-jig-saur grid (page 90)

Directions

- Tell students to imagine they are paleontologists trying to unjumble pieces of a dinosaur. Tell them that there are usually not many clues to help them.

- Talk about jigsaw puzzles. Ask, "How do you know where to place each piece? What is the largest number of pieces you can put together? 50? 100? 500? What clues do you look for?" (e.g., corners, edges)

- Have students look at the worksheet with the nine dinosaur pieces. Their challenge is to cut these out and arrange them to make the body of a dinosaur. Each one is marked with a clue to help them. (e.g., Middle 2) Ask, "What does this mean?"

- Have students look at the 3 x 3 grid. Discuss the different labels for the columns and rows. Explain how to cut out each dinosaur piece one by one and glue it onto the matching space on the grid.

- When the last piece has been placed, their dinosaur should be complete. Have them color it in, although no one knows exactly the actual color of dinosaurs.

Variations

- Students draw their own 3 x 3 grid and draw an interesting picture on this grid. (e.g., their favorite pet) Students cut up this grid, one square at a time, writing a clue on the back of each square. (e.g., Right 3) A friend puts their picture back together by following the clues.

- As a super challenge, students design even larger grid puzzles. (e.g., 3 x 6, 4 x 4)

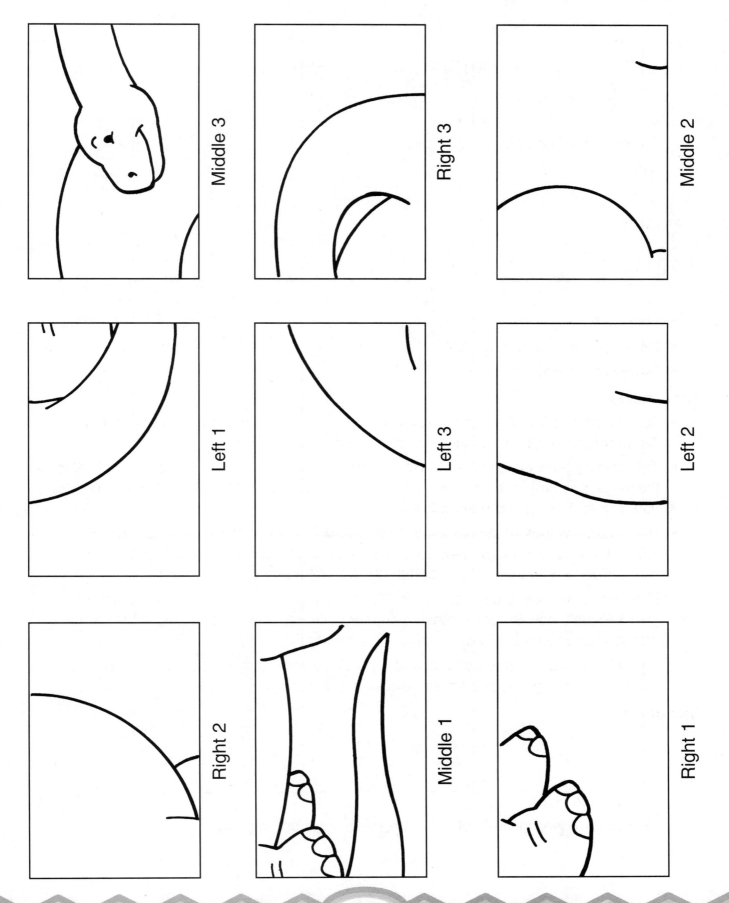

Middle 3

Right 3

Middle 2

Left 1

Left 3

Left 2

Right 2

Middle 1

Right 1

	Left	Middle	Right
1			
2			
3			

Take Me There

Skill

- Describe positions on a simple grid

Grouping

- small groups
- pairs

Materials

- pencils
- paper
- Take Me There grid (page 92)

Directions

- Ask students, "What are special features of the area where you live?" (e.g., shops, a river, farms) Ask, "What other features would you need to record if you were drawing a map?" (e.g., roads, railways, bridges)

- Say to the students, "Tell the person next to you how to get from your house to somewhere else in your neighborhood." (e.g., Go to the end of the street and then turn right.)

- Discuss the Take Me There grid. Ask, "What do the symbols stand for?" (e.g., The car might represent a parking lot. The boat might be on a lake or a river. The hot air balloon may be a base for early morning flights.)

- Have students imagine they are the person in the bottom left corner. Ask, "Where would you like to visit on your map?" (e.g., the duck pond) Ask, "If you can only move to the left or right and up or down, how could you get there?"

- Discuss directions together. (e.g., Move two spaces to the right. Go up two spaces. Go one space to the right again.) Ask, "Where are you? Is there another way?"

- Have students play with a partner where each has a grid. Have students start in the bottom left corner. Tell them to give instructions for their partner to follow, then exchange roles.

Variations

- Students color in their paths as they create a permanent record of their wanderings.
- Students create their own grid maps of their area.

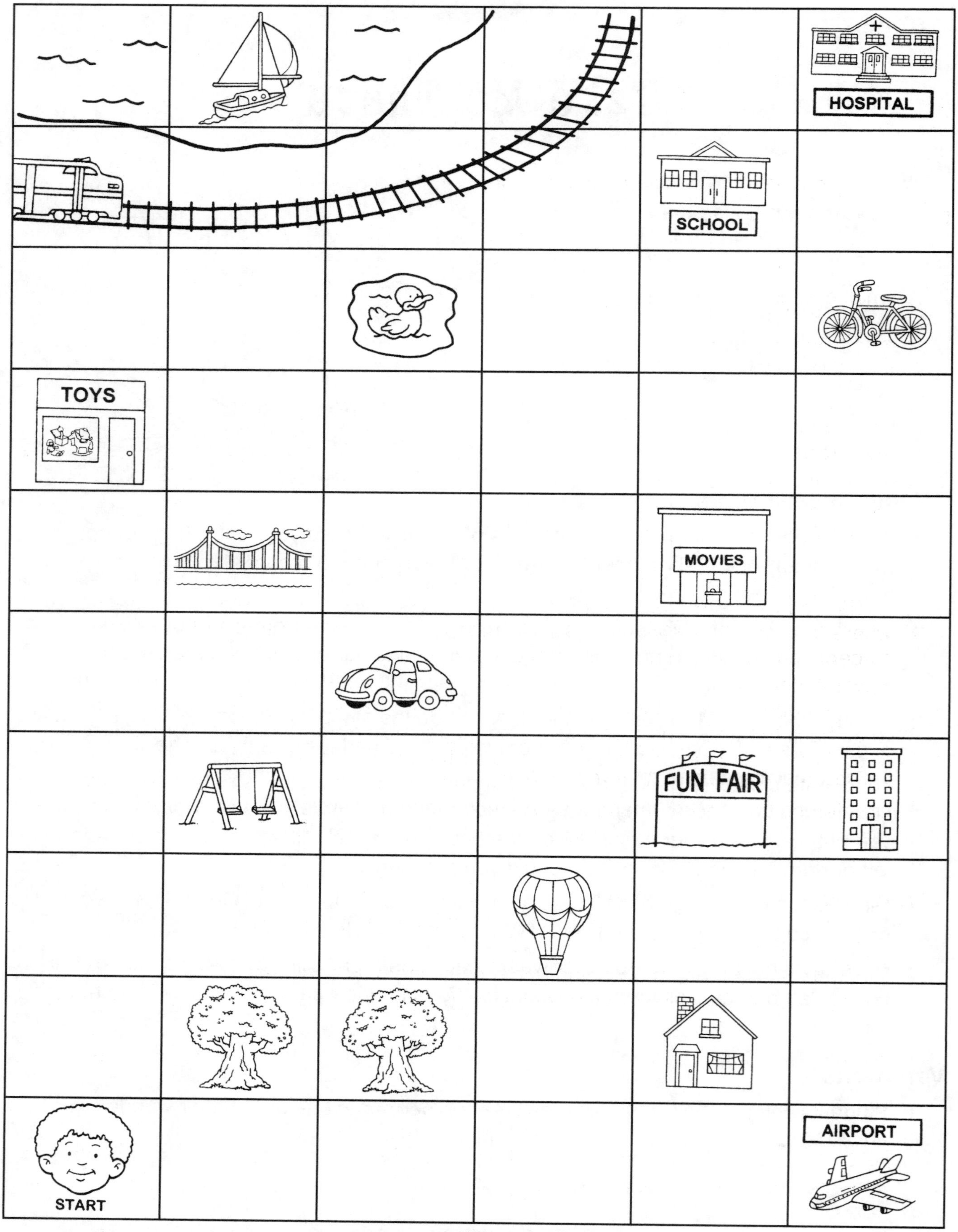
HOSPITAL
SCHOOL
TOYS
MOVIES
FUN FAIR
START
AIRPORT

Find the Treasure

Skill
- Use coordinates to describe positions on a simple grid

Grouping
- small groups
- pairs

Materials
- counters in two colors (e.g., red and black)
- paper and pencils
- Find the Treasure grid (page 94)

Directions
- Tell students that long ago, cargo ships carried silver, gold, and precious objects around the world. Shipwrecks were common. Tell them that some people believe treasure can still be found on a deserted island.
- Have students look at the island map. Say, "Describe what you can see." (e.g., a volcano) Ask, "Where would you hide treasure on this island?"
- Have students look at the grid. Discuss the labels for each column and each row. Explain how to name each space by reference to these labels. (e.g., C4 is the space where column C and row 4 intersect.) Tell them these are its coordinates. Have students practice pointing to and naming grid spaces using coordinate labels.
- Have students play a partner game. Have each student take a grid map and some colored counters. Have them sit so that their map cannot be seen by their partner. (e.g., back to back) The leader hides some treasure at random on his or her island. (e.g., four black counters) The other player tries to find this treasure by calling out coordinate clues. (e.g., Is it on D5?) If incorrect, the student marks this spot with a counter, so he or she remembers that he or she has asked it. Have students continue marking spaces on the map until all the treasure is discovered.
- Have students exchange roles.

Variations
- Students play a small-group version with the leader in the center and the other players facing out in a circle.
- Students play a more challenging game by hiding only one piece of treasure.
- Students play an easier game by drawing up a smaller grid, (e.g., 3 x 4), labeling the columns and rows and drawing their own island.
- **Secret Code**
  Students work with a partner. They draw a 5 x 5 grid and label the columns A to E and the rows 1 to 5. Then, they write in all the letters of the alphabet at random in the 25 spaces. Have them write *z* (the 26th letter) in the same space as *q*. Tell students they now have their own alphabet code. Have them write secret messages to each other in code; only they will be able to decipher them!

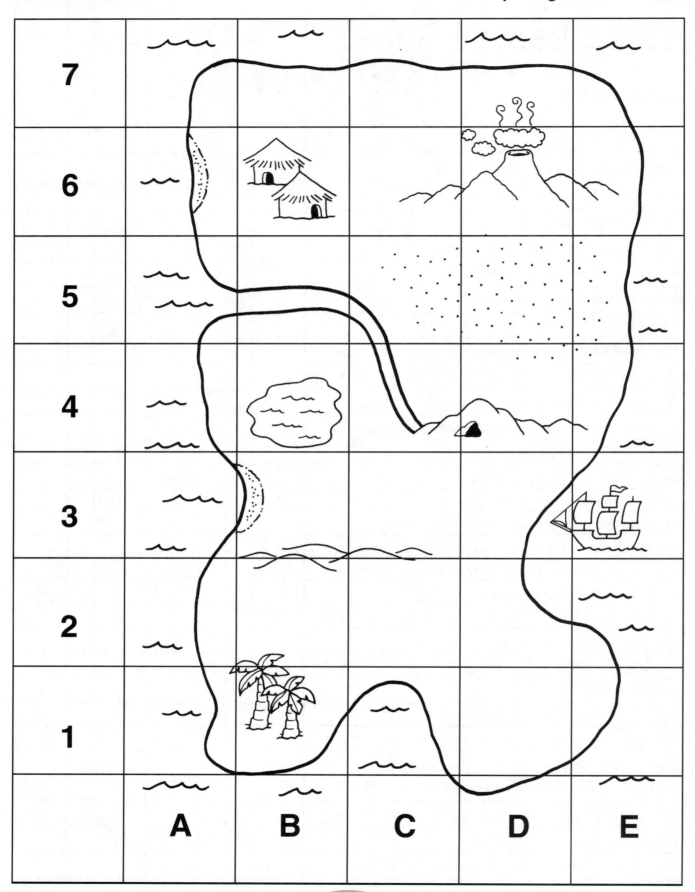

Skills Record Sheet

PRE-GEOMETRY

NAME

Skill										
Sort, match, name, and draw 2-D shapes										
Identify corners and sides on 2-D shapes										
Identify 2-D faces of 3-D objects										
Sort, compare, and describe 3-D objects										
Recognize and name simple 3-D objects										
Match 3-D objects with 2-D drawings and photographs										
Identify and create straight and curved lines										
Make patterns using a variety of lines										
Make, describe, copy, and extend patterns using 3-D objects										
Identify, continue, and predict 2-D patterns										
Flip, slide, and turn 2-D shapes to construct patterns										
Tessellate 2-D shapes to make patterns										
Identify matching halves in a 2-D shape										
Identify lines of symmetry in a 2-D shape										
Identify, make, and continue symmetrical patterns										
Identify, count, and describe faces/edges/corners of 3-D objects										
Construct 2-D shapes through body movements and games										
Construct 2-D shapes using sticks										
Construct and model 3-D objects using a variety of materials										
Use informal position language										
Describe the position of an object from different points of view										
Use the terms *left* and *right*										
Describe and follow simple directions										
Describe the position of an object in models/pictures/sketches										
Construct a model from memory/verbal instructions/diagrams										
Draw an object from different points of view										
Describe, follow, and draw a path on a simple map or maze										
Describe positions on a simple grid										
Use coordinates to describe positions on a simple grid										

Sample Weekly Lesson Plan

STRAND: Space
GRADE: 1

SUBSTRAND: Position
TERM: 3   **WEEK:** 5

LANGUAGE
- *to the left of, to the right of*
- *in the middle, on the top, on the bottom*
- *next to, beside, near*
- *from above, from below, from the front, from the side*
- *first, second . . . last*

OUTCOMES
- Describe and follow simple directions
- Describe position of an object in models, pictures, and sketches
- Construct a model from memory, verbal instructions, and diagrams
- Draw an object from different points of view

RESOURCES
balls, beanbags, hoops
spinners (page 78)
scissors

construction materials
activity cards (pages 81/82)
cloth (e.g., dish towels)

pencils
paper

MONDAY	TUESDAY	WEDNESDAY	THURSDAY	FRIDAY
• Whole Class: Review position vocabulary. (e.g., *left, right, front, back*) Ask students, "When do you use this language?" • Outdoor Group Activities: A: beanbags B: balls C: hoops In pairs, call out instructions to their partners. (e.g., "Use your left hand and roll the ball under your legs.") • Whole Class Game (What's My Direction?): (e.g., Everyone runs to the left and crawls around the tree.)	• Whole Class: Review position vocabulary. (e.g., *left, right, front, back*) • Partner Activities (Robots on page 77): Have students instruct their partner how to move around an area. (e.g., three steps to the left and turn right) • Small Group Activity (Robots spinner game): You will need spinner, cards, ball, beanbag, and a hoop for each group.	• Whole Class: (Dinosaur Bones on pages 80–82) • Group Activities: Use four blocks each. A: Yes/No B: Look Alikes C: Under the Cloth D: Talk to Me • Repeat activities with four to five blocks. • Dinosaur Challenge: Ask students, "Which team can construct the largest dinosaur in three minutes?"	• Whole Class: (Dinosaur Bones on pages 80–82) Line up model dinosaurs. Discuss positions (e.g., *left, right, middle, first, last*) • Group Activities: Use four blocks each. A: Yes/No B: Look Alikes C: Under the Cloth D: Talk to Me • Repeat activities with four to five blocks.	• Whole Class: Discuss model dinosaurs. Ask students, "How could you recognize one in a drawing? What are the key features?" • Partner Activity: Use four blocks each. • Draw Me (page 83) variation. Discuss and compare models. Then have students exchange roles. • Review position language. Repeat partner Robots game.

96